The *Wise Guide* series

1. **Advice for later life** - support and entitlements for over-65s
2. **Extra help at home** - essential advice for over-65s to live independently
3. **Healthy, happy, connected** - support and advice for older people living alone

As this book shows, there are lots of things we can do to stay healthy, happy and connected - whatever our stage of life.
A good place to start is to think about the five common ways that help us enjoy life:

- Keeping in touch with your family and friends.
- Learning new things - from a new language to a singing group.
- Giving your time as a volunteer, a good neighbour or helping family.
- Staying active - from joining a walking group to getting an allotment.
- Taking notice by keeping up with current affairs, finding out what's going on locally or getting online.

This *Wise Guide* aims to help you plan ahead for older age. It also suggests ways to keep in touch, keep active, get involved and enjoy life to the full. Ideas range from simple, practical things, from a daily walk in the park or trip to the library, right through to joining a group or signing up to study astronomy.

I'd love to know what you think of this *Wise Guide*. Please write to me at the address on the back cover or email janet.morrison@independentage.org.

Warmest wishes

Janet

Janet Morrison
Chief Executive, Independent Age

Contents

1. Staying connected as you get older

2. I've always wanted to...

3. Doing something for others - volunteering

4. Looking after your physical health

5. Looking after your emotions

6. Befriending

7. Care and connecting

8. Coping with loss

9. Advice for worried relatives

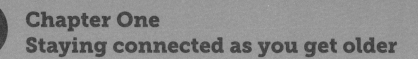

For many people, a key change in life comes with retirement - whether you and/or your partner are retiring. If you have always worked, you may find that with retirement comes freedom, choice and - most precious of all - time. But are you finding you miss the routine of work and the company you had there? Perhaps although you looked forward to having more time, the days can now seem very long.

When you plan ahead, it's good to think about the little things as well as the big ones. If you are moving to a new place, what will you do when you get there? If you are leaving friends and neighbours for a new life in the country, how will you make new friends?

To move or not to move?

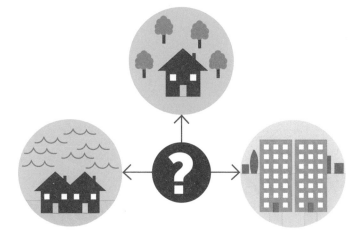

If you are planning a big change, such as moving house, you could think about how you will keep in touch with friends and relations, make new friends, get out and about and manage if you become unwell or less active? Even if you aren't planning a move, you could think about where you live now. Have you got friends locally? If you live in a rural area, how will you get about if one day you can no longer drive?

Many people like the idea of retiring to the country for the peace and quiet, but sometimes the country can be just a bit too quiet! While living in a town might be less picturesque, transport links will be better and the shops, libraries, doctors and other services more local. So, a move to the country needs careful consideration. There are useful factsheets about this at overthehillcampaign.org.uk, 01432 344039.

Look after yourself

If you have any health concerns at all, don't just accept this as part and parcel of getting older - make an appointment to see your GP or optician (see chapter 4).

Money worries

Perhaps you are worried your money won't last. Perhaps you are already struggling or have debts but feel you can't talk to anyone about it? Well, the good news is that there is lots of financial advice and help out there for you. But you do need to ask for it.

The Pension Service (0800 731 7898, Northern Ireland, 0845 601 8821) can work out if you are eligible for extra money over the phone. You will need to have your National Insurance number and all income and savings details handy. They may be able to visit you at home if you can't use the phone or are housebound. See also our *Wise Guide, Advice for later life*, which is packed with useful and up-to-date advice and information on how to boost your income and save money.

Keep in touch by phone

A long chat with a friend or relative over the phone is still the best substitute for actually being with them. But if you are worried about money, you might find you are restricting the number of calls you make to reduce your phone bill.

It's worth knowing that if you are on your phone provider's (such as BT or Virgin) regular tariff you are probably not getting the best deal. You can save a lot of money - sometimes £100s a year - by signing up to a call package that means you only pay a certain amount every month, your calls during the day and at weekends are often free.

"I make all my phone calls to friends and family in the evenings after 6pm. My phone tariff allows me free evening and weekend calls to local and national landline numbers as well as mobile numbers for up to an hour. To save being charged if I get near the hour limit, I hang up and dial again to get another free 60-minute call."

Betty, 80

Call your provider and ask what deals they have available. Ask them to explain anything you don't understand - information about tariffs can be very confusing. If you are online, you can look at all the phone companies and what they charge and find the best deal for you. It's a competitive market and companies are all trying to outdo each other on the best deal. You can usually earn an extra discount for signing up online. Have a look at homephonechoices.co.uk.

moneysavingexpert.com/phones/home-phone-calls#quicktips is a website that offers tips and advice on ways to save money in all kinds of different ways, including phone calls, utility bills - that's gas and electricity - and on insurance packages.

If you want to phone someone overseas regularly, there are special deals for this too. If you are confident online, it's worth finding out how to make phone calls using Skype. This means you can phone for free. If the other person is also online and uses Skype then you can even see each other. Skype is a very cheap way to stay in touch with friends and family who have moved away (skype.com).

It's free if you call computer to computer, but there is a small charge to call from your computer to a phone - UK calls cost £3.44 for 400 minutes a month at the time of going to press, but there are different rates for different countries.

It's in the diary - forward planning

> **Bob's story - pack up your troubles**
>
> The doctor told Bob he could do anything in moderation, "I do what I can do and I don't overdo it. You can do what you want. You need to get out and about and not sit and mope."
>
> Bob travels the country to visit his sisters and keep his social life active. If you book in advance, train travel can be cheap, especially if you can book online and a month in advance (trainline.co.uk).

It can help to plan your day and week ahead and put things in your calendar or diary to do each day - calling a friend, a walk in the park, going to a local café, library, community or sports centre, places of interest or the cinema... If there is something you have always wanted to do, then why not try and find out if you can learn how to do it locally or join a local group?

The Women's' Institute (**020 7371 9300, thewi.org.uk**) runs many interesting events and is very sociable, while the Mothers Union (**020 7222 5533, themothersunion.org**) is more closely affiliated to the Church of England. Both organisations do a lot of fundraising for charities and support people in local communities, and both have branches almost everywhere, including rural areas.

Other groups for women include Townswomen's Guilds, (**0121 326 0400, townswomen.org.uk**), and the National Women's Register (0845 450 0287, nwr.org.uk), which is a discussion and debate club. Couples or individuals might like to join Rotary Clubs (01789 765411, rotary.org), which hold many social events.

Back to work?

Are you missing work? Many people miss the routine and company of work. If you are missing it and are fit and well then there's no reason why you shouldn't go back.

Perhaps you could return on a part-time basis or teach your skill or retrain to do something totally different? There is plenty of advice on how to go about getting back into work at ageuk.org.uk/work-and-learning/looking-for-work/?gclid=CM_fm8CK6LYCFU3KtAodQmgASA. You might also like to think about volunteering (see chapter 3).

"I use my bus pass every day and wherever I go, I always ask if there's a special price for pensioners. A café gave me a free coffee once when I told them I was 90!"
Arthur, Southport

Getting about

Driving is a wonderful way to get about but it's not the only way of travelling. Are you still enjoying driving and do you feel safe on the roads? If you are worried about your eyesight then you should get your distance vision checked or even take another driving test to check that you are as good a driver as ever. If you are feeling anxious about driving or have been advised to stop, it may be time to get to know public transport.

The good news is that using public transport will save you lots of money - bus travel is free for over 60s across the UK and local buses often go right to local shopping centres, hospitals and city centres. There are fewer buses in rural areas and you will need to have a better idea of bus timetables, but you should still be able to get to where you want to go. Getting out and about on public transport will keep you fitter than driving and for longer distance travel there are many good deals to be had on train and coach travel, especially if you can book in advance.

Find out about local transport in your area from Traveline (**0871 200 2233**, **traveline.info**), Trainline (**thetrainline.com**) and National Express coaches (**nationalexpress.com**).

Many of us have things we wished we'd done when we were younger but never had the time. Well, maybe there's a chance to do them now! Perhaps you'd like to learn to sail, play a sport or an instrument, learn a language, grow your own veg, build your own car, walk from coast to coast or learn how to play chess. Whatever it is you fancy there are bound to be others who feel the same. If you are not online already, the local library will help you research your interest.

Try something new

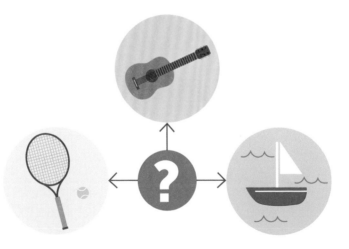

Did you know... the biggest regret people at the end of life have is not the things that went wrong in their lives but the things they didn't do.

'I wouldn't join anything for oldies'

Don't feel you have to join anything just because it's for people the same age as you. It might be worth going just to see if you like it but if you really don't fancy going then give it a miss. Instead, think of what you do like doing - being outdoors, walking, singing, and learning - and go for that instead. Perhaps you'd prefer to mix with younger generations - if so, you could think about volunteering or helping out at a school.

> "The local primary school asked the manager of our sheltered housing block if any of us would go and talk to the children about growing up in World War II, which they were studying. I had a wonderful time and have kept in touch with the school ever since."
> Annie, Sussex

Why not take up:

Walking

Rambling is sociable and there are groups all over the UK. The Ramblers Association is for everyone who likes to walk, whatever age. There are also other groups all over the UK for walkers of all ages and all stages of fitness, including for those with disabilities and those who want to take dogs, and walks that you can get to and home from by public transport.

- Ramblers Association England (020 7339 8500, ramblers.org.uk)

- Scotland (01577 861222, ramblers.org.uk/scotland)
- Wales (029 2064 4308, ramblers.org.uk/wales)

If you are disabled but still enjoy getting out and about in the fresh air, contact disabledramblers.co.uk, which researches and plans walks for people with all kinds of disabilities.

Gardening

You can make things grow even if you just plant a few fresh herbs in a window box. You might like to grow vegetables by making a patch in your garden or, if you are really ambitious, applying for an allotment. Your local council will have a list of allotments and there may well be a waiting list for them, so the sooner you find out the better. Birmingham, for example, has 115 allotment sites and over 7,000 plots. The National Allotment Society lists allotments all over the UK (01536 266576, nsalg.org.uk). Also, landshare.net is a food growing project that encourages people to share land.

Did you know... a B&Q Diamond card means over-60s get 10% discount every Wednesday.

Pets

Dogs don't have the reputation of being man's best friend for nothing. They are great company and keep you fit and secure. If you are considering getting a dog you do need to be fit enough to walk it twice a day, though, and be around for it. If you aren't sure whether dog owning is for you, many of the rehoming charities have walking programmes where you just take a dog for a walk. The Cinnamon

Trust (01736 757900, cinnamon.org.uk) specialises in helping older people with pets.

Whatever pet you get, you also need to consider how much attention it will need and the costs - particularly if you are getting a dog. It's definitely worth insuring any pet you get as vet's bills can be high but insurance can cost from as little as £5.00 a month.

The following charities are all looking for people to rehome dogs and cats. They can also advise you on animal healthcare, costs and on pet insurance.

Dogs Trust (020 7837 0006, dogstrust.org.uk)

Cats Protection League (08707 708 649, cat.org.uk)

RSPCA (0300 123 4999, rspca.org.uk)

Blue Cross (0300 777 1897, bluecross.org.uk).

Learning for fun

Is there something you have always wanted to learn? Maybe you've always wanted to learn Russian? Perhaps you are interested in film or art history?

If you are interested in learning pretty much anything just for fun, the University of the Third Age (U3A), which has been around for over 30 years, is a self-help organisation for older people no longer in full-time employment. Local U3A groups provide educational, creative and leisure opportunities in a friendly environment. There are groups all over the UK with nearly 300,000 members and meetings take place in a community hall or someone's front room. U3A also runs events for people who are on their own and these can be a great way to meet new friends.

All U3A groups are different as the skills and talents of their members define what they can offer, so if you find more than one local group in your area you would be advised to contact all of them to see what is on offer. The fun extends beyond learning and many older people find U3A forms the social hub of their retired life. They also run online courses for people who can't get out and about so easily or who are in residential accommodation (020 8466 6139, u3a.org.uk).

Going online

Evelyn's story

Evelyn has researched online the history of those lost during WW1 who came from Framlingham in Suffolk. Evelyn says, "There seems to be a large gap between those who have managed to 'keep up' with the vast changes in technology and those who, for instance, have not been able to learn how to use computers, mobile phones and even cameras. I am lucky to have two sons who have encouraged me!"

Many of us are scared of technology and the world of IT can appear confusing and daunting, but it really is easy to learn how to send emails or look things up on the internet. And once you know what you are doing, you may find that it opens a whole new world for you - as well as being a fantastic resource for finding things out, it can also be a way to make friends who have similar interests (Check out gransnet.com, bbc.co.uk/sport, ukhandknitting.com and fishing.com).

You can learn how to use a computer for free in the library or at your local Age UK branch. There are also many free courses to help you learn basic computing skills, such as emailing, shopping online and using Skype - making calls through your computer - which can be a really cheap way to stay in touch with friends and family who have moved away. Even if you don't have a computer at home, your local Age UK, local libraries and community centres may have computers you can use for free.

Computer courses

Age UK runs computer courses all over the UK and most are free. The courses avoid jargon and explain things clearly in plain English. They offer easy-to-follow training with the aim that as many of us as possible ultimately enjoy the advantages of computers and the internet.

Here are some options to get you started:

- call Age UK's free phone number 0800 169 6565 for your nearest Age UK branch and ask about local training opportunities
- ring the BBC First Click helpline to find a course near you on 08000 150 950
- ask at your local library or council about computer training opportunities
- find out about training events Age UK runs September and March every year.

Hazel's story

Hazel bought her first computer 13 years ago after her husband died. She says, "I was feeling a bit lonely and my daughter suggested I get a computer. I took computer courses through my local council. I went partly for the company, but mainly because I like learning new things. It's made a great difference because instead of just sitting at home watching television every night, I'm sat talking to friends online."

Back to the past

How much do you know about your own family history? Perhaps you'd like to find out more and trace your family history or the history of your local area. If you are online, there are many websites now that will help you do this (try ancestry.co.uk), but you can also start your research at your local library. The librarians will help you use the computers.

Perhaps you are more interested in the history of other families? Look at joining English Heritage (english-heritage.org.uk) or the National Trust (nationaltrust.org.uk). Both organisations are very reliant on the support given them by volunteers of all ages.

Did you know... the average cost of visiting a National Trust property is £6.50.

"I moved to Meanwood 40 years ago. Around that time I became interested in my family history and spent two years writing about my own family background. Since then I've written a lot of 'little books' and leaflets about the history of Meanwood and I help with the Leeds Civic Trust photo archive."
Doreen, 91

Follow the arts

Do you like theatre or listening to music? Perhaps you like to watch or maybe even take part in a local group. If so, why not think about joining a drama or operatic group? You could find it really fun. Some local theatres run groups especially for older people. At West Yorkshire Playhouse in Leeds (0113 213 7296, wyp.org.uk), for example, the Hey Days club is an opportunity for older people to meet, develop new creative skills and share them with others.

Sing a song

"The singing is wonderful. I love it."
Sonia, on her singing class at Open Age, London

"I think the key to enjoying older age is a good set of lungs and a positive attitude to life!"
Alice, 85

Making Music (020 7422 8280, makingmusic.org.uk) encourages all kinds of music groups and individuals to be part of a vibrant multi-cultural music scene. It has over 3,000 members and lists choirs by region. Choirs.org.uk lists 3,073 British choirs with websites and/or email contacts as does nationalassociationofchoirs.org.uk.

Did you know... both the Odeon (odeon.co.uk) and Vue (myvue.com) cinema chains offer very discounted screenings for people aged over 65 - sometimes with tea and biscuits thrown in.

Free-events.co.uk lists events such as races, carnivals and outdoor gatherings of all types all over the UK.

Local community activities
Whether you have a yen to do yoga, fancy a dalliance with dance or have a passion for Pilates - have a look first at your local library, community and local newspapers as well as national groups to find out

what's on close to you. You may be surprised to find how much is going on in work hours near you. Local colleges may run a wide range of day and evening classes that are easy to get to, interesting and affordable.

"My advice to anyone would be to find a local library or somewhere where there is information about groups that meet - something you are interested in. These things can help. If you're feeling down it can be very difficult to take that first step, to reach out, but it's important that you do."
Matthew, 70

Have a look at the range of evening or day courses available at your local college (hotcourses.com). There may be anything and everything from knitting to Mandarin.

Keeping the faith

If you have a faith then you know where to look for comfort when you feel low. Whatever your religious beliefs are, your faith and the friends you have at your place of faith can be a huge support to you - as can your minister, priest or other faith leader. You have much in common and they are there to offer comfort and support, and you can trust them.

Your place of faith will not only offer you the comfort of worship but potentially friends of all ages, social outings and events. Make the effort to go, let them know if you are struggling and ask for help to get there if you need it. If you can't manage that or if you are unwell then most faith leaders will also come to your house to worship with you. You only need ask.

If you are unwell or can't get to church services, many now have a system whereby you can listen to the service on the phone. Ask your faith leader if this is possible at your place of worship.

"I got involved in a church where there's an old people's lunch group and fellowship meeting. I go out a lot. I go to prayer meetings and church societies. I also run a singles group, Christian Friendship Fellowship. Sometimes I do feel alone - I get the blues, if you like. I just praise God and that gets me out of it. I can't imagine not having a faith. It's inside me."

Averil, 69

Starting something new

You might feel nervous about taking on something new, especially if you are doing it on your own. Is there someone you know who might like to come with you to a new activity or who might accompany you just until you have made some new friends?

One advantage you have in starting something new is that there are many discounts you can make the most of once you are over 60 or 65 - free bus pass, discounts on entrances to cinemas, theatres and exhibitions, long distance bus and railcards (see page 13). There are lots of things you can do for not very much cost.

It's nice to do something for a good cause or other people and volunteering can also be a great way of making new friends. Volunteering is about giving your time to do something useful without getting paid (apart from expenses).

People who volunteer tend to love it. They feel they are contributing something, are busy and needed, meeting new people and making such a difference to the people they help. You can do as much or as little as you feel like doing.

Did you know... nearly 4.9 million people aged 65 and over in England take part in volunteering or local community activities. In the UK, four in every 10 people over retirement age volunteer regularly.

What kind of volunteering is for you?

Many national organisations have volunteer programmes so, for example, if you want to work with animals you might contact the RSPCA; if you like the arts then contact your local arts centre, gallery or theatre to see if they have a volunteer's scheme. Is there a stately home or garden near you that needs volunteers? If you like to be out in the fresh air then why not see if your local garden centre needs help?

What skills do you need to volunteer?

Absolutely none. Don't worry that you might not have the right skills to volunteer - you almost definitely will have if you can do any of the following:

- drive
- answer the phone
- do simple sums
- make tea
- be an extra pair of hands
- sit and chat with someone
- be friendly
- accompany someone on a trip
- help someone get on line or make sense of his or her bills, or
- be someone's eyes or ears or a strong arm to lean on.

If you have expertise in business, management, marketing or accounting, Reach (reachskills.org.uk/for-volunteers) finds volunteer positions for people with specific skills.

Other sites that might be helpful and are also packed full of news, views, discounts and opportunities for older people, include silverhairs.com and laterlife.com.

The Retired and Senior Volunteer Programme, (020 7643 1385, csv-rsvp.org.uk) helps older people use their life experience in their community and especially welcomes volunteers over 80.

If you want to look around for what's in your area and you are online, have a look at Do It (do-it.org.uk). Find the nearest centre to you and look at the organisation that needs help. There's bound to be something for you.

Some charities support older people and rely on volunteers of all ages. Contact Independent Age (020 7605 4200, independentage.org), Royal Voluntary Service (0845 601 4670, royalvoluntaryservice.org.uk/get-involved/volunteer) or Age UK (0800 169 8787, ageuk.org.uk/get-involved/volunteer).

Contact the Elderly (0800 716 543, contact-the-elderly.org.uk, see page 54) holds tea parties for older people over 75. The tea parties are provided by hosts who can offer tea for small groups two to three times a year. The charity also relies on regular volunteer drivers to take guests to the tea parties and home again.

There will also be local charities in your area that run shops, offer befriending services - where you spend time with someone and keep them company on a regular basis - run day centres and so on. All of them will be looking for people just like you!

Professional skills?

If you are a professional or have specific skills, you might think about getting involved with a local Time Bank (timebank.org.uk). You provide your time, for example, gardening or decorating - and earn a credit, then someone else offers their skills to help you, say, set up your internet. No money is involved.

There are around 250 time banks in the UK so far. (01453 750952, timebanking.org).

> ### Sonia's story
>
> Sonia volunteers one morning a week. She says, "My husband died 12 years ago and I gave it a year and then volunteered. I had been a medical secretary so I was of some use on the phone. I have met the most wonderful people and we go on holidays together. It has been wonderful meeting other people in the same boat as me. I felt I must do something. I can't sit here feeling sorry for myself.
>
> "I feel I am doing something useful, though I am a small cog in a big wheel. I am lucky at 90 that I still have all my faculties. I just need someone to bring me here and take me home."

What to check when you volunteer

- where to volunteer - try searching on the Do-it database
- whether they will pay your expenses (eg travel)
- if you have a clear idea of what you will be doing
- if you get training and support.
- if there's something in it for you - new skills, fun, and a chance to contribute to a cause?
- how much time you are expected to give, and how many times a week or month

- that you have the chance to ask questions - don't be shy about asking questions as you go through the process of applying for an opportunity.

"I volunteer for the Royal Voluntary Service (previously called WRVS) and I visit Dawn who is partially sighted and spend time with her. I change light bulbs, do her cashbook for her and help her with her ongoing battle with her Skybox!

"I'd say we're friends - we talk openly and I like that. She could call me at any time. It's nice for me as I also live on my own. Let's face it, if you are a volunteer you are getting something out of it as well."

Simon, London

Open Age (020 8964 1900, openage.org.uk) runs over 200 weekly activities for older people in the London boroughs of Kensington, Chelsea and Westminster, including groups for men and support for older people to get to activities.

It'll be harder to take up the opportunities in the first two chapters of this book if you're not feeling your best. This chapter is about doing everything you can to stay well. The better you look after yourself, the more likely you are to feel positive, stay active, get out and enjoy life.

It is important that you eat well and regularly, drink plenty of fluids and not too much alcohol. When you live alone, cooking a meal for one can seem like a major effort and you might not even bother to make a cup of tea if there's no one to share it with. Perhaps you could share your lunch with someone once or twice a week or go to a café now and then for a change. You might also see what lunch clubs there are locally and pop in once or twice a week.

Check ups

Whether or not you have any health problems, you could find out if your surgery has any regular check-ups or surgeries for over 65s - many do. NHS Choices (nhs.uk/Livewell/Screening) lists what tests and screening sessions are available to over 65s.

You can also call NHS Direct (0845 4647) for advice and information on all health matters.

If you have a particular health problem that is restricting what you do and may be long term, you could also ask your doctor if there are any organisations that can give you more advice and support on how to manage it in the future. For example, Bowel and Bladder Association helpline (**0845 345 0145, bladderandbowelfoundation.org**); British Lung Foundation BLF helpline (**03000 030 555, blf.org.uk**); Diabetes UK helpline (**0845 120 2960, diabetesuk.org**).

Flu jabs

Flu jabs are free for you if you are over 65 and save lives. Find out when your surgery does them and book yourself in.

Eating to stay healthy

As you age, your digestive and immune systems become less efficient. You need to eat well and nutritiously to get the most out of your food. If you eat little and often and drink enough fluids, you can prevent blood sugar swings and dizziness that can lead to falls. Eating well also keeps your leg and hipbones strong, which can help you recover after a fall or operation.

What is a healthy, balanced diet?

If you have diabetes, arthritis or high blood pressure, your GP or dietician will have told you which foods to eat or avoid. In general, try to include these key elements:

What	Source	What it does
Fibre	Fruit, veg, oats, brown pasta, brown rice, wholemeal bread, beans, lentils	Prevents constipation, lowers cholesterol
Vitamin C	Citrus fruit, veg especially peppers	Helps ward off infection
Vitamin D	Oily fish, eggs, spreads, sunshine	Keeps bones healthy
Calcium	Canned fish, nuts, seeds, broccoli	Keeps bones healthy
Protein	Lean meat, fish, chicken, cheese	Helps maintain muscle mass
Zinc	Shellfish, meat, bread	Boosts immunity and recovery
Iron	Red meat, dried fruit, cereals, leafy green veg	Fights anemia, helps circulation
Omega 3	Trout, salmon, sardines	Keeps heart and nervous system healthy and reduces symptoms of conditions like arthritis

Did you know... you can get your recommended 'five-a-day' from dried, frozen or tinned fruit and veg. Dried fruit like apricots have valuable amounts of fibre and iron. Freezing preserves vitamin and mineral content. Tinned produce also counts, providing you buy fruit tinned in juice, not syrup, and veg tinned without added salt and sugar. All are usually cheaper than fresh produce.

If you have a poor appetite or find it hard to keep weight on

You might feel hungrier by making your meal look appetizing and by not overloading your plate. Don't drink with meals as the liquid will fill you. Other tricks are: add butter or spread to potatoes and veg; have a milky drink instead of tea and coffee and use full fat milk instead of water to make up soup, jelly or porridge.

And if you are trying to keep weight off...

If you are too heavy three small, healthy snacks between your meals will help prevent you from getting ravenous, then overeating. If you are underweight, snacking will help you to take in enough calories without overloading your stomach. But these snacks shouldn't be chocolate digestives. Include some protein: try beans on toast, a small piece of cheese on an oatcake or a hard-boiled egg (weightwatchers.co.uk).

"After my husband died, the evenings were very lonely. I didn't feel like making a proper dinner so I'd snack on cheese and biscuits then eat chocolates in front of the television. I put on three stone! I joined a Rosemary Conley slimming club and started exercising twice a week. It wasn't the diet that helped me lose weight so much as getting out of the house and meeting new people."
Tessa, 72

Cooking for yourself

If you can't open cans or pour the kettle, there are numerous gadgets to help you, from electric tin openers to kettle tippers. The Disabled Living Foundation (**0845 130 9177, dlf.org.uk**) can advise. If you're no longer able to shop and cook, could you order supermarket groceries, including frozen and ready-made meals on the internet or ask a relative to arrange this for you? If you are unable to prepare meals for yourself, phone social services and ask for a free community care needs assessment. There is much more information on getting a needs assessment in our *Wise Guide, Extra help at home*.

Did you know... dehydration can lead to dizziness, making you more prone to a fall. Make sure you drink enough fluids like water, tea, coffee and diluted fruit juice or squash. Plenty of fluid also helps prevent constipation.

Don't fancy eating alone?

Ask social services, Age UK and at your library about older people's luncheon clubs. Some branches of the Salvation Army (020 7367 4500, salvationarmy.org.uk) run luncheon clubs with transport provided as well as drop-in centres and cafes providing nutritious meals and snacks.

Supermarket restaurants tend to be good value. Many pubs, hotels and cafes offer pensioner deals and reduced price Sunday lunches. At Wetherspoon's pubs (jdwetherspoon.co.uk) the menu includes calorie counted meals and meals for people on special diets.

Whatever happened to meals on wheels?

"Delivering hot meals daily proved expensive and impractical. Today, you're more likely to get a 'man with a van' delivering two weeks' worth of frozen meals plus a counter-top oven or microwave for you to heat them up in. If your council provides this service, you may only qualify if it considers you have 'substantial' or 'critical' needs and you may have to contribute financially. Ask social services for a free care needs assessment. But remember, most supermarkets will deliver and have a great choice of ready-made meals like soups, lasagne or curries at reasonable prices. Just check they aren't too salty."

James, Independent Age

Dental and mouth health

If you are avoiding fruit or meat because of a sore mouth or ill-fitting dentures you may not be getting enough Vitamin C and iron. A good dentist should be able to help. To find an NHS dentist, call NHS direct (**0845 4647, nhsdirect.nhs.uk**), in Scotland contact NHS 24 (**0845 424 2424, nhs24.com**). Mouth ulcers may be the result of a Vitamin B12 deficiency. See your GP or pharmacist.

Prevention is better than cure

You know yourself better than anyone and keeping yourself well is also about anticipating what's increasingly likely to go wrong, and taking steps to prevent it! So as well as thinking about your health now, are there things you can do to make your home safer? For example, if your balance is a bit wobbly you could remove rugs and other trip hazards and think about installing handrails where they would help.

Help getting around

If you are losing your balance or have had a fall you might well be as worried you might fall or trip outside. If you are concerned then you could talk to your GP who will have some ideas as to equipment that could make all the difference to your confidence - such as a handrail for slippery outside steps, rails indoors, a walking stick or walking frame.

Your GP can advise you on whether you might get any aids you need from social services or need to buy your own. There are many firms who sell helpful aids and equipment. If you are in England, try Eden Mobility (0800 652 8444, edenmobility.co.uk), which also has a number of shops up and down the country. See our *Wise Guide, Extra help at home*.

Keeping active

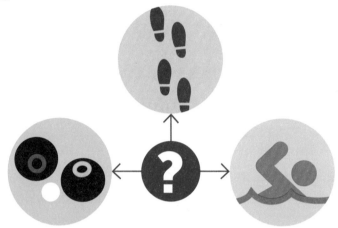

If you have always been active then it is probably part of your routine, whether you are a walker, swimmer or tennis player. But keeping active is not so much about sport as just keeping your joints moving. Walking, stretching... whatever exercises you like to do will all help you keep fit. Just do a bit of any exercise that gets you up on your feet and bearing the weight of your own body and it will help to keep the muscles active, bones strong and maintain strength and balance.

You could visit or call your local sports centre or gym to find out what classes you might like to take part in. Many local authorities also run fitness classes and activities for over 65s and many are free. Pilates and yoga, for example, are based on gentle exercise and are very popular.

Keep in the swim

Swimming is great exercise because it is non-weight bearing and many pools have special sessions for older people or for women only. If you can't swim, you could sign up for lessons or have a go at aqua aerobics - exercise in the water.

Keep track of what you drink (alcohol units)

Research recommends no more than 11 units a week for older people. A unit is half a pint of beer or a small glass of wine.

Most of us like a drink - and it's not just younger people who can drink more than is good for them. More and more people over the age of 55 are being admitted to hospital with alcohol-related health problems. You may also find now that it takes only one or two drinks to lose balance, strength and judgement, and falls have more serious consequences the older you are. It's also worth watching how much you drink if you are on your own. One glass might cheer you up but three or four can make you feel maudlin and sad.

Five good reasons not to drink too much as you age:

• heavy drinking makes you more prone to a fall
• drink fills you up but provides no nutrients
• alcohol is a depressant
• as you age, your ability to process alcohol changes
• alcohol can be dangerous - even fatal - combined with drugs like painkillers.

Check with a pharmacist that it's safe to drink alcohol with the medicines you're taking.

Keeping an eye on your eyesight

It is very common for both sight and hearing to weaken as you get older so it's a really good idea to make an appointment with your optician to get your eyes tested at least every two years and, if you already wear glasses, make sure they are comfortable and clean. There are other things you can do to look after your eyes:

- get your doctor to check for problems, such as high blood pressure or diabetes
- make sure lighting is good (clip lights that attach to books can help)
- use eye drops or artificial tears to keep the eyes lubricated and comfortable
- get an electronic reader which can magnify text to much larger fonts and even provide backlighting.

Keeping your ears open

Your hearing is very likely to deteriorate as you get older. If you are having to turn up the telly or are missing what people are saying, ask your GP to test your ears and to check why. You may simply have a wax build-up or you might need a hearing aid. If you do need a hearing aid, they are very discreet these days and you may be eligible for a free one.

There is lots of advice on looking after your health. If you have a hearing problem:

- find out about other hearing support services and devices such as telephone amplifiers

- protect your ears - avoid loud noises and use headphones with care.

Failing eyes and ears?

Are both your eyes and ears letting you down? The charity, Sense, estimates that there are 220,000 people over the age of 70 with a condition known as 'dual sensory loss' in the UK. This means that both your eyes and ears are not as strong as they were.

You may think that failing hearing and sight is just a normal part of aging but there are lots of things that can help, from practical tips to equipment and a special assessment from social services.

Get in touch with Sense in England, Wales and Ireland (**0845 127 0066/020 7520 0972**, sense.org.uk), or Sense Scotland (sensescotland.org.uk).

Getting better after an illness

It's rotten being ill but keeping in good spirits and staying optimistic helps keep you generally well and recover faster from illness. Don't lose touch with friends and neighbours - let them make a fuss of you. You may be able to return the favour some day. The sooner you can get back onto your feet after an illness, the more likely you are to make a full recovery.

Home from hospital

Sometimes you need a bit of help to get well again after an illness or a stay in hospital. Your local social services department may offer short-term help. Your local council may also provide you with low cost or free meals on wheels service for a short or longer time. The Red Cross also offers short-term support and may lend you any equipment you might need (redcross.org.uk).

Take a break

They say a change is as good as a rest, so whether you fancy a weekend in Wales or your budget allows you to cruise the high seas, why not make the most of the advantages you have of being to go away at any time? Look for cheaper low season holidays and make the most of the many transport discounts available to you once you are over 60.

You might feel anxious about travelling alone or want to travel somewhere exotic but not on your own. If that's the case, why not take the plunge and consider going on a group holiday?

These types of holidays can be a great way to experience new places and cultures and to meet new people. There are many companies that specialise in group holidays, while specialist holiday group Saga (saga.co.uk) offers older people's holidays of all types. If you are worried at the thought of travelling alone, have a look at laterlife.com/laterlife-holiday-companion.htm.

Specialist holidays

Sense, the sight and hearing charity, runs a holiday programme for older people - Holiday Plus (0845 127 006) - a week-long holiday for older people who need additional support to access and enjoy a break.

"The days are very long when the walls are the same."
Jane, Yorkshire

"As a soldier and expedition leader I've met many courageous people. Most were hardy and self-reliant but I think the bravest of the lot were those who could ask for help when the chips were down. We all need to understand when we need rescuing. We may not like it, but we aren't made of metal and don't function like computers."
Sir Ranulph Fiennes, explorer

We all like to have friends and people to care for and who care for us. But as life goes on it's easy to lose some people along the way. Giving up work, losing someone you love, friends and family moving away and your local community changing can all reduce the number of people you see regularly and it's not surprising if this can leave you feeling lonely and low. Also, sometimes, you can feel low for no reason that you can put your finger on and when that sadness doesn't go away, it could be depression.

What is depression?

Everyone feels low sometimes but when that lowness persists or if you feel low when there's no concrete reason for it, then you may be depressed. Depression means the feeling you have when you feel sad, anxious, hopeless, negative and helpless and these feelings don't go away.

Depression can also take a toll on your physical health because when you are depressed you often don't sleep well or you sleep too much; you don't eat enough or you eat too much. Being depressed can mean you are more prone to infections or you don't bounce back quickly after an illness.

Did you know... you are not alone if you feel depressed. Depression is very common and affects people of all ages and in all walks of life. Overall, it affects two in every 10 men and three in every 10 women aged 65 or over.

Our top tip

If you think you may be depressed, talk to someone about it. It can be hard to take the first step but it will be such a relief to share how you feel with someone.

Contact your GP

If you don't have anyone you feel you can talk to, make an appointment to visit your GP and tell him or her how you feel. Usually your doctor will offer either medication or the chance to talk to a counsellor - or both.

Your GP might refer you to another NHS service called Improving Access to Psychological Therapies (IAPT) (iapt.nhs.uk), which will offer you someone to talk to and help you find new ways to manage your low mood and other problems you may be experiencing, such as feeling worried, anxious or panicky. All IAPT services are free and confidential and there is no upper age limit.

"It's true that as we get older we face challenging experiences and these can really affect how we feel but the therapies we offer can really help people who are struggling to cope better and manage their feelings in a way that can improve their quality of life."

Soo Lincoln - manages part of the IAPT service in Leeds

Margaret's story

Margaret went to see her doctor about another problem and when he asked her how she was feeling she started crying. Her doctor recommended the IAPT service and gave her a number to call.

"I didn't know what to expect really but I did feel awful and I didn't want to burden my friends or family with it, so I contacted the number and they arranged an appointment near to where I live. I started seeing my therapist once a week and then once I started to feel better, once a fortnight.

"I learnt lots of ways to deal with how I was feeling and what was happening to me. I could just say exactly what I felt without worrying, whereas you tend to put a show on for other people. It helped to be able to talk and also to get good tools and ideas and I started to feel a lot better."

If your doctor prescribes anti-depressants, do ask him or her what side-effects they have and how long you might have to take them as you need to take them for a few months for them to work.

If you feel you would like to talk to someone but don't want to go through your GP, The British Association for Counselling and Psychotherapy (BACP) lists registered counsellors all over the UK. The costs vary from around £35 an hour to much more, though some counsellors will charge less if you are on a low income.

> **Our top tip**
> Do make sure your counsellor is registered by checking with the British Association of Counsellors and Psychotherapists (01455 883300, itsgoodtotalk.org.uk) and that you feel comfortable with him or her.

Depression Alliance is a self-help group for people with depression (0845 123 2320, depressionalliance.org). National mental health charity, Mind (0300 123 3393, mind.org.uk), produces free downloadable self-help booklets, *How to cope with loneliness* and *How to manage stress*, which are really helpful. But there are many other ways to beat depression and increase self esteem.

Things you can do for yourself

You might not want to talk to anyone about how you feel. You might feel happier just doing what you can until you feel a bit brighter, but do try to do something. Perhaps just spend 20 minutes each day doing something in the garden, going for a walk, sorting out photos or writing your thoughts down so that you achieve something each day. People recover from the most severe depression but it may last a long time and you may need medical or psychological help to make a full recovery.

A day at a time

Try taking each day at a time and appreciating the good things you have while acknowledging the things you don't like and, if you can, doing something about them - a step at time. This is a new approach called 'mindfulness' (bemindful.co.uk) and it can help you when you are feeling really low.

Be creative

Writing a diary about your feelings, painting and making things can be really absorbing and can make you feel you are doing something constructive. Writing and art sometimes help you express how you feel without the need for words.

"If people have a faith or even a meditation routine it may be very valuable to practise this both by themselves and with others. Both bring a feeling of connectedness."

Madeleine Böcker, therapist, London

Finally, if something is troubling you and you have no one to talk to about how you feel, call the Samaritans (08457 90 90 90, samaritans.org).

Chapter Six
Befriending

If you feel lonely or unhappy some of the time and just wish you had someone to chat to, you may want to think about having a befriender. It can make a huge difference to how you feel.

> "Loneliness just creeps up on you. None of us think it will happen to us, but suddenly it's there - you are on your own."
> Ros, Independent Age

What do befrienders do?

Befrienders are usually volunteers who come to your house, take you out or call you over the phone regularly.

Independent Age offers three different types of befriending services:

Volunteer visitors are caring volunteers who make regular visits to your home to sit and chat over a cup of tea or take you out for a walk, a bit of shopping or a visit to a museum. Many volunteer visitors are older people themselves so it is very likely you will be matched with someone you have things in common with. Call 020 7605 4200, or visit independentage.org if you think you might like a volunteer visitor.

Telephone Buddies is a phone befriending service for those who find it difficult to get out or just prefer to talk on the phone than face-to-face. A volunteer calls weekly or monthly for a chat at an agreed time for as long as you need them to. Contact Rosalind at Independent Age (020 7605 4232, rosalind.devine@independentage.org) if you think you might like a telephone buddy.

Live Wires is a popular telephone book and discussion club where you are called once a month or so to enjoy a lively discussion on books, films or a topic decided by the group, with around six other older people. The discussions are facilitated by a volunteer and Independent Age provides the books and films for free. All you need is a landline or mobile telephone. Contact Rosalind at Independent Age (020 7605 4232, rosalind.devine@independentage.org) if you think you might like to join *Live Wires*.

William's story

William, 81, joined *Live Wires* over two years ago. He says, "I really enjoy the telephone group. I live alone and, though I'm lucky in so far as I can still get out and about, in the last few years many friends have died and others have moved away so you can find yourself knowing less people.

"The telephone group is really rather fun. We read all kinds of books - thrillers and all sorts. It's a pretty good selection and the conversation flows very well. It really motivates me to read a wider variety of books. I can honestly say I look forward to it every month."

Age UK can also link you up with a face-to-face befriender, and they also provide a telephone befriending service. *Call in Time* (0800 169 6565, ageuk.org.uk) consists of a regular daily or weekly phone call.

Charlie's story

Charlie hit it off with his Age UK befriender Glynis from the start. He says, "We hit it off straight away. It was marvellous. We both had the same sense of humour. Now we talk about anything - people we know, friends, episodes that have happened to us - all sorts of things. We get on well together. It's made life much more pleasant, much nicer. I look forward to her coming.

"Also, it's a strange thing to say, but when you're old, you tend to become a bit dirty around the house. But because Glynis is coming round every week, I make the effort to keep on top of things."

Community Network (020 7923 5250, community-network.org) also runs friendship groups on the phone for up to six people.

"I have been living alone for the last 13 years and feel very lonely, which is not a good feeling. The Community Network groups have been fantastic - talking on the phone about my situation with others really helps. I have made new friends who I intend to stay in contact with. I would love to meet up with them. Picking up the telephone once a week for an hour has really revitalised my life."

Leslie, Southampton

Sunday Best

Even if you are busy all week, you might find that Sundays can be the most difficult to get through if you are on your own. Contact the Elderly (0800 716 543, contact-the-elderly.org.uk) runs tea parties in England, Scotland and Wales one Sunday a month for people over the age of 75. The tea parties are for small groups and are hosted by regular volunteers in their homes. Guests are picked up by a volunteer driver and taken safely home again afterwards.

While hosts run one or two parties a year, the drivers who pick the guests up will often be the same for months and years, and so acquaintances turn into friends and loneliness is replaced by companionship. The tea parties are a real highlight for many older people who live alone and for whom Sunday can be the loneliest day.

Contact the Elderly tea parties - what the guests say:

"It keeps us going. We all need to feel wanted - that's why we're all staying so young!" Doris

"They're right good dos. It's lovely at the party and the hosts couldn't do better if they were my own." Horace

"Weekends are the worst. It can get pretty dull when you live alone - it's the time when you think of families all together and that's hard. They make you feel so welcome at the tea parties." Margaret

"It's always in the diary - it's changed my life. I'm meeting new people. I really look forward to it every month." Gloria

Ruth's story

After losing her husband six years ago, Ruth, from rural north Wales, eventually got in touch with Contact The Elderly. She says, "The tea parties are happy occasions and the volunteers look after us so well. There's lot of chatter and noise. I really look forward to them." Ruth has even started helping the coordinator of the group by liaising with the other older guests over the telephone, giving her the chance to chat to people who are local.

Other organisations offering befriending services are Royal Voluntary Service (0845 600 5885, royalvoluntaryservice.org.uk) and the Befriending Network (0131 261 8799, befriending.co.uk).

Support for everyone

Maybe you are feeling alone because you have no one you feel you can talk to about your sexuality. You may have spent your working life without anyone knowing - you wouldn't be the only one! Maybe now is the time to talk to someone. You can get support at Age UK (ageuk.org.uk/health-wellbeing/relationships-and-family/older-lgbt-communities).

"Thanks to spending time with my volunteer, I feel more confident about attending other events without him. I feel I should have been doing something about meeting more people like me years ago."

Michael, Luton

LGBT (which stands for Lesbian, Gay, Bisexual and Transgender) Age Scotland supports people by matching them with volunteer befrienders who are also part of the LGBT community so that they can spend time in non-judgmental company. It also tries to raise awareness of the community so LGBT people get the choices and dignity they, like all older people, deserve. LGBT Age Scotland (0131 523 1107, lgbthealth.org.uk/content/lgbt-age) currently operates the befriending service across the Lothians and also offers monthly social events for people over 50. These are open to anyone who can travel to the venue.

If you're in London, contact openingdoorslondon.org.uk/befriending.html.

The London Lesbian and Gay Switchboard (not just for people in London) offers advice and information for all ages on all aspects of LGTB life and sexuality (0300 330 0630, llgs.org.uk).

If you live in the UK and are from another part of the world, you may be able to link up with people from your culture via a place of worship or community centre. It will probably have information on what else there is in your area or nearby for older people. Your local council may also be able to help you.

Tower Hamlets Friends and Neighbours befriends people in Tower Hamlets, London (020 8983 7979, thfn.org.uk). Its clients are from a wide range of different cultural backgrounds and are often over 75, living alone or have been diagnosed with dementia. Here is what some of them say about their befrienders.

"I get emotional support. They have endless patience with me."

"I get a lot of help with paperwork and have someone to share my troubles with."

"It's a friendship to help me talk things over. It's beneficial because I know I can trust that person."

As we get older, health problems - whether our own or of a close friend or relative - can become bigger factors in our lives. This chapter suggests ways to help you stay connected, whether you're caring for a loved one or have care needs yourself.

Meeting people in the same boat

If you're a carer or have a particular health problem, could you join a support group for people in the same situation? Carers' associations, like Carers UK, (020 7378 4999, carersuk.org), offer get-togethers and friendship. If you, or someone you love, is affected by Alzheimer's, arthritis, Parkinson's disease or cancer, the appropriate charity will give you a chance to contact others.

The Grandparents Association (0845 434 9585, grandparents-association.org.uk) offers support to people who are bringing up - or unable to see - their grandchildren.

Caring alone?

When you care for someone, it can be physically and emotionally draining and you may not have time to give your own needs much thought. But it is really important that you do take time to look after yourself as well - you will feel better and will be able to care better.

Just the nature of caring can be very lonely, but there is a lot of support for carers now either through your local social services or Carers UK (**0808 808 7777**, carersuk.org). With their help you should be able to find some respite from caring and take some time to have a holiday every so often. It can help just to have a regular phone call to a carers' helpline or with someone who has time to listen to you.

The Carers Trust (**carers.org**) also offers advice, information and runs services all over the country for carers.

Daphne's Story

Daphne cares for her husband and their life together is planned around his dialysis. "Being a carer has been the most challenging and stressful role I have ever taken on in my life. It has not been an easy journey, and one encounters continual demands. Nevertheless adopting objectives to cope has proved a necessary ingredient to manage daily life.

"Last year, I joined the University of the Third Age, an Age UK weekly walking group and a reading group. I also started supporting Carers UK and the Campaign to End Loneliness, which has made me feel that I am doing something really worthwhile with my life."

Live-in companions

Need a little help around the house and perhaps some companionship? If all you need is a little extra support to remain in your home, the Homeshare scheme may be able to pair you with someone who needs somewhere to live. There are schemes in Cumbria, Bristol, East Sussex and London. Visit sharedlivesplus.org.uk/homeshare.

"I share my home with an Australian nurse. In return for shopping, some cooking and light housework, she lives rent-free. We share bills. I love the company."
Margaret, Yorkshire

Upstairs downstairs

If you are really struggling to cope at home, you might make life a bit easier for yourself with more support or by adapting it so you can manage it better - and your friends can too.

For more advice and information see our *Wise Guide, Extra help at home.*

There may come a point when you have to make big decisions - like whether at some point you may want to move house or into sheltered accommodation. It's good to think about the big decisions before you actually have to make them. There are a lot more options than just care homes - have an early look at the sheltered or residential accommodation your area just to see what you think of the choice on offer.

"I moved at age 74 to an active residential complex so that as I got less active I would not be isolated and lonely. This has worked very well and I am thankful I made this move while I was still able to build myself a new life in a new community of people. Now I am less active I have the companionship of other residents in our communal lounge where we can have tea and coffee any time, and can hold birthday parties, wakes for fellow residents who have died, film shows, Christmas festivities, fish and chip suppers and so on.

"We have a house manager, so though I am a widow with no children, I always have someone there if I am in need of help or counsel. This was an important move for me, and though such a 'downsizing' is hard work, it is worth doing before it gets beyond one's capabilities to carry through. I hope my last move will be from here feet first!"

Penny, 82

Chapter Eight
Coping with loss

By the time you retire you may already have lost friends and relatives - your parents, for example. Losing someone you love is always hard but to lose your partner is probably the biggest loss to bear.

Everyone grieves in different ways and there is no time limit on how long it takes. You may never get over the loss of your partner completely. Things may never feel the same again but there are people out there who can help you come to terms and cope with the loss.

It's an old cliché that it's good to talk, but a true one. You may not feel like talking to anyone at first or you may feel like talking all the time. Either way is completely normal. It can help to express how you feel, though. If you are not able to talk, think about writing down how you feel or of memories of your partner - you might find this comforting.

There are times when you might not want to share how you feel with close family or friends. If so, you might consider talking to a specialist bereavement support worker from the specialist bereavement charity, Cruse.

Bereavement support

Cruse Bereavement support workers are specially trained to work and support bereaved people of all ages. You can be referred to Cruse via your local GP or by calling its national helpline or branch nearest to you. If you are in Scotland, contact Cruse Scotland.

Grief on losing a life partner is long term, but Cruse offers someone to turn to and suggests ways to make it easier to cope. They will listen to you for as long as it takes and offer a national helpline or face-to-face support. Cruse offers services that are tailored to each person. The national branches can give face-to-face support and the helpline offers a listening ear.

"Don't be afraid to ask or pick up the phone - the help is there."
Paul Williams, bereavement support volunteer

Cruse Bereavement Care offers free information, advice and support to bereaved people. It provides a telephone helpline and face-to-face support. In England and Wales, contact 0844 477 9400, crusebereavementcare.org.uk, in Scotland (0845 600 2227, crusescotland.org.uk) and in Northern Ireland, contact 0844 477 9400, cruse.org.uk/northern-ireland).

Our top tip
Be kind to yourself - there is no expected time to get over bereavement.

Other support

Lifeline provides support for people in distress and despair in Northern Ireland. It can also provide follow-up support, including counselling and complementary therapy (0808 808 8000, lifelinehelpline.info).

London Friend LGBT Bereavement Helpline is a dedicated helpline offering support and practical information to lesbian, gay, bisexual and transgender callers from anywhere in the UK who have been bereaved or are preparing for bereavement (020 7837 3337, londonfriend.org.uk/bereavementhelpline).

National Association of Widows is a membership organisation that offers support, friendship and understanding to men and women who have lost their partners (0845 838 2261, widows.uk.net).

Samaritans offers confidential support for people who are despairing or suicidal. Lines are open 24 hours a day (08457 90 90 90, samaritans.org).

Comfort in memories

At first, you might find that memories are too painful to bear and photos just upset you, but in time they can bring great comfort. When you are ready, it can help to have a special time or place where you remember the person you've lost. You might like to visit the grave or go somewhere you both loved, listen to music or plant his or her favourite flowers.

If you don't feel like talking to anyone about your loss but feel alone then you might like to read the helpful books. Mind, the mental health charity, publish books on bereavement and other subjects that deal with the emotions you might feel after a bereavement (mind.org.uk).

If you are feeling really low, do go and see your GP who can refer to counselling services or find a counsellor for yourself at bacp.co.uk (see chapter 4).

Someone to talk to

As time goes on you may start to feel like doing things again and picking up your social life but it can be hard to start doing things again on your own.

If you are a widower, it can be even harder as not only have you lost your partner but also you may be struggling to learn new skills, like cooking, getting around if your partner did the driving and cleaning the house.

If you are from a different culture, the loss of a partner can leave you feeling very isolated and lonely - especially if family and friends are overseas. Do try to stay in touch with them by phone. You could call the Samaritans (08457 90 90 90, samaritans.org), talk to your GP or visit your place of worship and talk to them there about how you are feeling. They may well be able to put you in touch with some local help.

There are many agencies that offer befriending to bereaved people wherever you are from - just someone to call you once in a while or to visit you if that's what you'd prefer. Befrienders can also take you out and help you start to build confidence again.

Age UK and Royal Voluntary Service both have befrienders who work with bereaved people.

> ### Betty's story
>
> Betty lives in west Wales. Ten years ago she lost her beloved husband Ken to cancer. "I coped reasonably well because I had a good son who was close, but then he was diagnosed with cancer. Really, the end of my world seemed to have arrived. I thought, I can't live without my son, my world is empty."
>
> But then she met Elaine, a Royal Voluntary Service volunteer befriender who visits her two or three times a week. "I wouldn't swap her for the world," Betty says. "Really, in my life there is nobody to replace her. She lifts me completely, she really does. When the phone rings and it's her at the end of the line, it's a great feeling. You feel as if you're wanted. I could be very lonely without her, that's for sure. Very lonely. She fills a big space."

"Mum was Dad's social life; he supported her but didn't have any interests of his own. When she died suddenly at 71, he was devastated. I went through his diary for three weeks after her death and wrote something in it for each day, from a haircut to a coffee morning."
Sally, Cardiff

Perhaps you are reading this *Wise Guide* because you are concerned about an older relative or friend. You might be worried that they are lonely or feeling down - you might just be looking for ideas to help them get more out of life. There are many things you can do to help them, though it is important that you consult with your relative or friend at every stage rather than making decisions for them!

While you may feel your relative isn't coping at home so well, it is a fact that most older people chose to remain at home as long as possible and even when they become more frail. If that's the case with your older relative then there is lots you can do to help them stay at home for as long as they can manage independently or with some support from you or other sources.

On the home front

A good place to start is by seeing how well they are managing at home. Do they see friends and manage to get out and about or are they spending a lot of time on their own and feeling low because of it?

Your relative might not raise these things, but you can. Just ask how they are feeling; if there is anything troubling them or anything that they need? They will appreciate your concern and, hopefully, a chance to talk about things.

If you ask someone how they feel. It gives them a chance to tell you and if things aren't so good, you have the opportunity to listen, offer comfort and perhaps some practical help too. The website gov.uk has lots of advice and information about independent living, services and support, including lunch clubs, day centres, meals on wheels and fitness.

You should also contact your local council to see what it offers in the way of services for older people and how you can go about supporting your older relative to get it. The council will also have information on lunch clubs, day centres, meals on wheels and other services that may help your older relative feel less lonely or isolated.

Have a look at our *Wise Guide, Extra help at home - essential advice for over-65s to live independently* (020 7605 4225, independentage.org).

Cooking

If your older relative or friend is struggling with opening tins and pouring kettles there are numerous gadgets to help them, from electric tin openers to kettle tippers. Contact the Disabled Living Foundation (0845 130 9177, dlf.org.uk).

If they are finding it difficult to shop or cook, or perhaps just don't feel motivated to cook a meal for one, perhaps you could order - or show them how to order - supermarket groceries, including frozen and ready-made meals on the internet.

If they cannot prepare meals at all then you could phone your local council's social services department and ask for a free community care needs assessment.

Health checks

Is your older relative or friend getting more frail? Are they eating properly and drinking enough and taking whatever exercise they can manage? (see chapter 4). Do they seem low-spirited or are they confused? If you think they may have a physical health problem or may be depressed, then - with their permission - book an appointment with the doctor/optician/dentist and go with them for reassurance. If they are happy for you to do so, they will probably appreciate your company. It might be helpful for you to take notes so that you can discuss the doctor's advice with your relative afterwards.

"After Mum died I noticed that Dad didn't seem to have any interest in anything anymore - not even in his grandchildren, music or cricket, which he'd always been passionate about. We could see he was lonely though he didn't want to admit to it and he refused all offers of help from neighbours and friends, and even from us!

"While he wouldn't let us do as much as we would have liked, my brother and I kept in touch by phone, visited every weekend, shopped for him, made his lunch and stayed with him for as long as we could so he had some company at least once a week. It wasn't an easy thing to manage - we lived a long way away from Dad (who didn't want to live with us!) and both of us had young children. But if we hadn't made the effort I don't think he would have seen anyone from one month to the next. I still feel we didn't do enough, but that was his choice."

Lily, Devon

Befriending

Your visits to your older relative or friend will be so welcome, but maybe it's not enough, particularly if they are housebound. Perhaps you could help them make some new friends through befriending. Befrienders are people - often volunteers - who spend regular time with another person. A regular visit from a befriender can be the highlight of a lonely person's week (see chapter 6).

Thinking of caring?

The decision to care for an older relative either by living with or supporting them at home or, more commonly, having them come to live with you is one that involves not just the two of you but your whole family. You need to consider all the pros and cons of what can be a life-changing decision for you and your elderly relative. It might be very helpful for you to talk to other carers about their experiences before you dive in.

You can also find lots of help and advice on how to best support your older relative as well as read the experiences of many carers at Carers UK carersuk.org or NHS Choices (nhs.uk/Livewell/Disability/Pages/Olderrelative.aspx).

Dementia

If your relative has been diagnosed with dementia, there is still much you can do to help keep them fit, well, active and living as normal a life for as long as possible. But you will need information about the illness and what may happen in the future so that you are prepared and can find the best support for your relative as and when he or she needs it.

Your first point of call could be the Alzheimer's Society (0300 222 11 22, alzheimers.org.uk), a care and research charity for people with Alzheimer's disease and other forms of dementia, and their families.

Dementia cafés - advice and support over a cuppa

A diagnosis of dementia does not mean the end of a social life for people with the diagnosis. Dementia cafés now exist all over the UK and provide a safe place for people with dementia to meet in café-like surroundings, and get advice and support. Guideposts Trust (0845 437 9901, dementiaweb.org.uk) provides specialist information and care services for people with dementia and their carers, and will be able to advise you about the availability of dementia cafés in your area.

If you would like more information about Independent Age's services, please fill out the form below and return it to:

Freepost RLTT-ACRZ-LZZT, Independent Age, 6 Avonmore Road, London W14 8RL

I would like more information on:

How to access Independent Age's services:

- join a telephone book or discussion club ☐
- get a volunteer to visit me at home ☐
- get a 'phone friend' who calls me weekly ☐

How to become a volunteer ☐

How to support Independent Age's work ☐

Name _____

Address _____

_____

Postcode _____

Phone number _____

Email _____

Data protection. We would like to contact you from time to time to keep you posted on our activities. Please let us know if you do NOT want us to do this.

Index

public transport **11, 13**